# SHARE A STORY

# The Train Ride

# Introduction

One of the best ways you can help
your children learn and learn to read
is to share books with them. Here's why:

• They get to know the **sounds**, **rhythms** and **words**
used in the way we write. This is different from how we
talk, so hearing stories helps children learn how to read.

• They think about the **feelings** of the characters
in the book. This helps them as they go about
their own lives with other people.

• They think about the **ideas** in the book. This helps
them to understand the world.

• Sharing books and listening to what your children
say about them shows your children that you care
about them, you care about what they think
and who they are.

*Michael Rosen*

Michael Rosen
*Writer and Poet*
*Children's Laureate (2007-9)*

For Michael Philip – J.C.

For Amelia – S.L.

First published 1995 by Walker Books Ltd
87 Vauxhall Walk, London SE11 5HJ

This edition published 2011

10 9 8 7 6 5 4 3 2 1

Text © 1995 June Crebbin
Illustrations © 1995 Stephen Lambert
Concluding notes © CLPE 2011

The right of June Crebbin and Stephen Lambert to be identified
as author and illustrator respectively of this work has been asserted
by them in accordance with the Copyright, Designs and Patents
Act 1988

This book has been typeset in Garamond Light Condensed

Printed in China

British Library Cataloguing in Publication Data:
a catalogue record for this book is available from the British Library

ISBN 978-1-4063-3501-9

www.walker.co.uk

# The Train Ride

Written by
## June Crebbin

Illustrated by
## Stephen Lambert

WALKER BOOKS
AND SUBSIDIARIES
LONDON · BOSTON · SYDNEY · AUCKLAND

We're off on a journey

Out of the town –

What shall I see?

What shall I see?

Sheep running off
And cows lying down,

That's what I see,
That's what I see.

Over the meadow,
Up on the hill,

What shall I see?
What shall I see?

A mare and her foal
Standing perfectly still,

That's what I see,
That's what I see.

There is a farm
Down a bumpety road –

What shall I see?
What shall I see?

A shiny red tractor
Pulling its load,

That's what I see,
That's what I see.

Here in my seat,
My lunch on my knee,

What shall I see?
What shall I see?

A ticket collector
Smiling at me,

That's what I see,
That's what I see.

Into the tunnel,
Scary and black –

What shall I see?
What shall I see?

My face in a mirror,
Staring back,

That's what I see,
That's what I see.

After the tunnel –
When we come out –

What shall I see?
What shall I see?

A gaggle of geese
Strutting about,

That's what I see,
That's what I see.

Over the treetops,
High in the sky,

What shall I see?
What shall I see?

A giant balloon
Sailing by,

That's what I see,
That's what I see.

Listen! The engine
Is slowing down –

What shall I see?
What shall I see?

A market square,
A seaside town,

That's what I see,
That's what I see.

There is the lighthouse,     The sand and the sea…

Here is the station –

Who shall I see?

There is my grandma

Welcoming me...

Welcoming

me.

# Sharing Stories

Sharing stories together is a pleasurable way
to help children learn to read and enjoy books.
Reading stories aloud and encouraging
children to talk about the pictures and join in
with parts of the story they know well are
good ways to build their interest in books.
They will want to share their favourite books
again and again. This is an important part
of becoming a successful reader.

**The Train Ride** is a colourful, rhythmic picture book telling the story
of a child's journey through the countryside to visit his grandmother
by the sea. Here are some ways you can share this book:

• The story is told in the rhythm of the train moving on the tracks. This adds to the pleasure of hearing it read aloud.

• Read it aloud a few times and invite your child to join in with the pattern. Leave gaps so that they can echo, "That's what I see" and "What shall I see?" Help them to match the words they say to the words on the page.

• Try reading the whole story together, passing it between you like a chant. You can read the words on the yellow background and your child can read the words on green.

• The story is told in words and pictures as if the reader is sitting in the train carriage on a journey with the characters. Talk together about the illustrations and what you "see out of the window". You could name and count some of the animals and explore some of the puzzles in the pictures, for example, why are the sheep running off?

• The strong rhythm in this story helps children when they come to read the book for themselves. Each time you read it together, encourage them to take on more of the reading.

# SHARE A STORY
## A First Reading Programme
### From Pre-school to School

**Beginnings – 2 years+**

Look Out, Suzy Goose — Petr Horáček

Walking Through the Jungle — Julie Lacome — Introduced by Michael Rosen

Hello, Goodbye — David Lloyd, Louise Voce — Introduced by Michael Rosen

Penny Dale — TEN IN THE BED — Introduced by Michael Rosen

THIS IS THE BEAR — Sarah Hayes, Helen Craig — Introduced by Michael Rosen

The Big Wide-Mouthed Frog — Ana Martín Larrañaga — Introduced by Michael Rosen

**Early Steps – 3 years+**

A New House for Mouse — Petr Horáček — Introduced by Michael Rosen

The Train Ride — June Crebbin, Stephen Lambert — Introduced by Michael Rosen

THE OTHER DAY I MET A BEAR — Russell Ayto — Introduced by Michael Rosen

Jane Chapman — Old MacDonald Had a Farm — Introduced by Michael Rosen

The Tiger and the Jackal — Vivian French, Alison Bartlett — Introduced by Michael Rosen

Zed's Bread — Mick Manning, Brita Granström — Introduced by Michael Rosen

**Next Steps – 4 years+**

The Hairy Toe — Daniel Postgate — Introduced by Michael Rosen

The True Story of Humpty Dumpty — Sarah Hayes, Charlotte Voake — Introduced by Michael Rosen

BEANS ON TOAST — Paul Dowling — Introduced by Michael Rosen

Over in the Meadow — A Counting Rhyme — Louise Voce — Introduced by Michael Rosen

Polly Dunbar — Dog Blue — Introduced by Michael Rosen

Introduced by Michael Rosen — Night-night, Knight And Other Poems — Michael Rosen, Sue Heap

**Taking Off – 5 years+**

"Have You Seen the Crocodile?" — Colin West — Introduced by Michael Rosen

HANDA'S SURPRISE — Eileen Browne — Introduced by Michael Rosen

The Ravenous Beast — Niamh Sharkey — Introduced by Michael Rosen

Allan Ahlberg, Colin McNaughton — One, Two, Flea! — Introduced by Michael Rosen

Nick Sharratt — Dinosaurs' Day Out — Introduced by Michael Rosen

The Old Woman and the Red Pumpkin — Betsy Bang, Rachel Merriman — Introduced by Michael Rosen

## Sharing the best books makes the best readers

**WALKER BOOKS**

www.walker.co.uk